Go For It Maths!
KEY STAGE 1

Let's Have Fun With Shapes

Practise and Learn with Games and Activities

By Mike Askew

Ruby Tuesday Books

Tips for Doing Maths with Your Child

- Find a quiet place to work with no distractions. Turn off the TV, music and screens.

- The activities in this book have been designed to help children learn about shapes, space and position while playing games and having fun. There are specific tips relating to each activity on pages 30–32.

- Do praise your child for specific mathematical things they do. If you say, *"That was really smart when you counted the sides on that shape"*, it will be more effective than *"You are clever"*.

- Do let your child teach you. Listen to how they are trying to do the maths and help them refine what they are doing before rushing to show them **your way**.

- Do treat getting stuck as a positive experience. **Yet** is a powerful word. *"I can't do it!"* can be turned around by saying, *"You can't do it – yet!"*

- Do stop work and put an activity aside if your child gets frustrated. When you come back to the activity the following day, they are likely to have fresh ideas.

- Avoid saying things such as *"Don't worry. I was never any good at maths."* Help your child develop a **can-do** view of learning maths.

Above all, treat all the activities playfully and enjoy them together.

Circle

Equilateral triangle

Scalene triangle

Square

Rectangle

Pentagon

Contents

Hexagon

Octagon

Trapezium

5-point star

6-point star

Line Designs

You will need:
- A sheet of paper
- A ruler
- A pencil
- Coloured pens or pencils

Use your ruler and pencil to draw straight lines on the paper.

Put the lines in different places and make them cross each other to make a pattern.

Keep drawing lines until you are happy with your pattern.

1 Look at your pattern.

Can you find any shapes with 3 sides?

If you can, colour them all in with the same colour.

2 Next, can you see any shapes with 4 sides?

If you can, colour them all in with a different colour.

Go For It!

Can you draw another pattern that has 3, 4, 5, 6 and 8-sided shapes in it?

3 Keep going! Look for shapes with 5 sides, 6 sides and so on. Colour each group in a different colour.

Shape Hunt

Get Ready

You will need:
- A ruler
- A pencil or pen
- Paper

Look at the rectangle.

How many rectangles can you find within the big rectangle?

I think there are 6 rectangles.

I think there are more than 6 rectangles.

Now look at this triangle.

How many triangles can you find within the big triangle?

GO FOR IT!

Use your ruler, pencil and paper to make up a puzzle like these and challenge a friend to solve it!

Take 4 Triangles

Get Ready

You will need:

- 2 squares of thick paper or thin cardboard (about 15 cm x 15 cm)
- A pencil or pen
- Ruler
- Scissors

Take your two squares and draw a line from corner to corner.

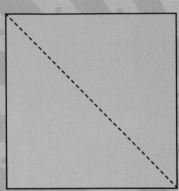

Carefully cut along the lines to make four triangles.

Now try fitting your triangles back together again to make other shapes.

Can you make these shapes?

- A big triangle
- A square
- A rectangle
- A pentagon (a shape with five sides)
- A hexagon (a shape with six sides)
- An octagon (a shape with eight sides)

Four's Fantastic Facts

The line from corner to corner on your squares is called a **diagonal**.

Diagonal lines

6

Two-Piece Tangram

You will need:

- A square of thick paper or thin cardboard (about 15 cm x 15 cm)
- A pencil or pen
- Ruler
- Scissors

Find the middle point on one side of your square. You can do this by measuring with a ruler.

Middle point

1 Make a small mark at the middle point.

Cut Here

2 Use your ruler to draw a line from the middle point to the opposite corner.

3 Then cut along this line to make a triangle and a four-sided shape.

Which of these shapes can you make with your two pieces?

- A big triangle
- A rectangle
- A pentagon
- A hexagon
- An octagon

Four's Fantastic Facts

Some of the most famous square-shaped puzzles are called tangrams. A tangram has seven pieces and might look like this.

Follow My Lead

You can make the shapes to play "Follow My Lead" by cutting them from paper or card. Make sure you have two of everything.

You can download a collection of shapes for printing and cutting here:
www.rubytuesdaybooks.com/goforit

8

1. Stand up the book to make a screen between you and your friend.

2. Make a design with your shapes behind the screen. Make sure your friend can't see your picture.

3. Now you must give your friend instructions so they can make your design on their side of the screen.

For example, you might say, "Put a green triangle above a blue circle."

4. When your friend thinks they have made your design, take away the screen to check.

Your friend's picture

The better your instructions are, the closer your two pictures should match!

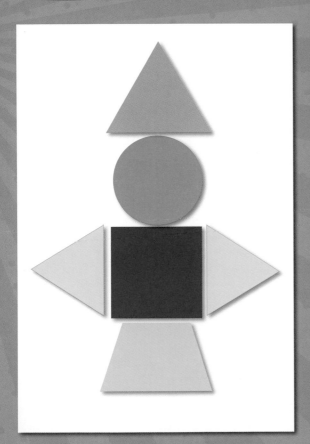

Your picture

Your friend can ask you questions if they are not sure what to do.

5. Swap over. Now your friend makes a design and you must follow their instructions.

9

Fill the Grid

You will need:
- Paper
- Scissors
- A red, blue and yellow pen or pencil

Cut nine little squares from some paper. The squares should be the same size as the squares on the grid below.

To fill the grid, you must draw each of the three shapes in the three colours.

For example, take one of the little squares you cut out. Draw a triangle on the square and colour it red.

Fill the Grid			
○			
△			
□			

Now place the red triangle on the correct square on the grid. We've done this one for you!

Now Go For It and fill in the rest of the grid!.

Go For It !

Try making up and drawing your own grid of shapes and colours.

Midpoint Patterns

Get Ready

You will need:
- Paper
- A ruler
- Coloured pens or pencils

1 Use your ruler to draw a triangle.

2 Now make a small mark in about the middle of each side of the triangle.

3 Join the marks together. You've made another triangle!

4 Now repeat Steps 2 and 3 on the new triangle.

What do you notice?

Keep going! You can colour in your pattern, too.

GO For It!

Now try doing this but start with a four-sided shape.

What happens if you try with a six-sided shape?

11

Exploded Square

Get Ready

You will need:
- A small square of coloured paper (about 15 cm x 15 cm)
- Scissors
- A sheet of white paper
- A glue stick

Follow the instructions to make your exploded square picture.

1 Fold the small square of paper in half.

2 Now carefully cut a strip off the edge of the paper. You should be cutting along the open edges, not the folded edge.

Make your cut wavy and interesting and make sure you are cutting through both sides of the paper.

Open edge

Folded edge

Cut a wavy line

3 Now cut off another wavy strip. Again, make sure you are cutting through both sides of the paper.

Folded edge

Pieces cut from the edge of the paper

Strips from second cut

Strips from first cut

4 Finally, cut off another wavy strip.

Strips from third cut

5 Unfold the creased piece of paper. Stick it onto the middle of your white piece of paper.

6 Now find the two strips that fit with the creased piece of paper. Glue the strips next to the middle piece, but leave a gap.

7 Find the next two pieces that match up with the edges of the pattern, and glue them onto the white paper.

Four's Fantastic Facts

A shape, design or picture like this, where one side exactly matches the other, is called **symmetrical**.

8 Finally, glue the last two strips in place. Your exploded square is complete!

Exploring Symmetry

Get Ready

You will need:

- An old magazine (check with an adult that it's OK to cut up the magazine)
- Scissors
- A sheet of paper
- A glue stick
- Coloured pens or pencils

Face Match

Find a picture of a face in a magazine. Look for a picture where the person is looking straight at you.

1 Cut out the picture. Then cut the face in half from top to bottom.

2 Glue half of the face onto the sheet of paper.

3 Use coloured pens and pencils to draw in the other half of the face.

Butterfly Match

Get Ready

You will need:
- A square of coloured paper
- A pencil
- Scissors
- Paints

Take your square of paper and fold it in half.

1 Draw half a butterfly on the folded paper.

Make sure the butterfly's body is against the fold.

2 Carefully cut around the outline of the butterfly and open it up.

3 Put some blobs of paint on one half of your butterfly.

4 Fold the butterfly closed again and rub over the outside to transfer paint onto the other half.

5 Open up your beautiful symmetrical butterfly.

It's a butterfly match!

Birthday Card Jigsaw

Get Ready

You will need:

- The front of an old birthday card
- Scissors
- A friend to play with

Use an old birthday card to make this fun jigsaw game.

1 Cut up the front of the birthday card into nine pieces.

Make each piece an interesting shape.

2 Mix up the pieces and lay them face up on the table.

3 Now, your job is to help your friend put the picture back together, like a jigsaw. You must give your friend instructions using shape, position and orientation words.

For example, you could say, "Pick up the rectangle with the giraffe's face. Put it in the top right-hand corner of the picture. Turn it clockwise so it is the right way up."

16

You must not touch any of the pieces!

Build a Box

Get Ready

You will need:
- An empty cereal box
- Scissors
- Masking tape or low-stick tape
- Paper and a pencil or pen
- An adult helper

You should now have 6 rectangles.

(See further instructions regarding cutting up the box on page 31.)

1 Ask an adult to help you cut the cereal box into sections. Only cut along the edges.

2 Now use tape to stick the 6 pieces back together. You need to make a flat shape that will fold up to remake the box.

Draw what your flat shape looks like.

3 Carefully peel off the tape.

Can you find a different way to join the 6 rectangles so that they still fold up to make the box?

Draw this arrangement, too.

How many different ways can you find to remake the box?

Four's Fantastic Facts

A flat shape that folds up to make a box is called a **net**.

17

Know Your Shapes

Square

Rectangle

Circle

Trapezium

Pentagon

Hexagon

Equilateral triangle

Scalene triangle

5-point star

6-point star

What's My Shape?

Get Ready

You will need:
- Lots of counters
- A friend to play with
- Paper and pens or pencils

1 Each player takes a big handful of counters and chooses one of the boards on page 19. Decide who goes first. They are Player One.

2 Next, each player chooses a shape from their board and writes down their choice, keeping it hidden from their opponent.
For example:
Pentagon/Big/Blue   6-pointed star/Small/Red

3 Each player must now guess their opponent's chosen shape by taking it in turn to ask a question.

4 Player One starts and asks Player Two a question about their shape. For example: **"Is your shape green?"**

If the answer is **"No"**, Player Two uses counters to cover up all the green shapes on their board that have now been eliminated. If the answer is **"Yes"**, Player Two covers all the red, blue, orange, yellow and pink shapes.

5 Then it is Player Two's turn to ask a question.

6 Keep taking turns until one player can guess their opponent's shape and win the game!

Here's an example of game play:
Player One: *Is your shape green?*
Player Two: *No*
Player Two covers all the green shapes on their board.
Player Two: *Does your shape have four sides?*
Player One: *Yes*
Player One covers all the shapes on their board that don't have four sides.
Player One: *Is your shape big?*
Player Two: *No*
Player Two covers all the big shapes on their board.

You can download the game boards for printing out here:
www.rubytuesdaybooks.com/goforit

Board B

Board A

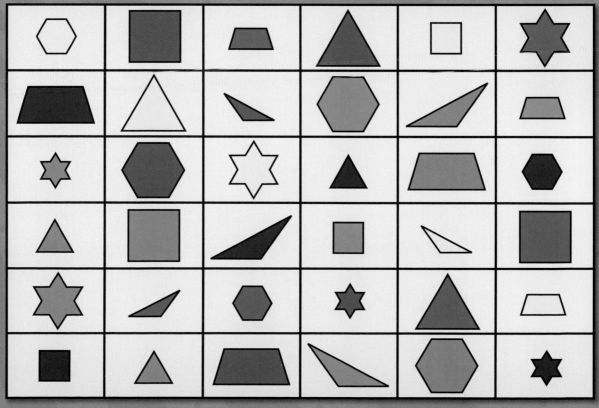

Player sits here

19

Square & Triangle Challenge

Get Ready

You will need:
- 20 cocktail sticks or pencils that are exactly the same length

Making Squares

These squares have been made using 12 pencils.

Can you see five squares?

Now it's your turn. Take 20 pencils or cocktail sticks.

What is the biggest number of squares you can make by putting them together?

If you're using cocktail sticks, you're not allowed to bend or break them.

Growing Triangle

Here are 3 pencils making a triangle.

Here is the next size triangle. It takes 6 pencils to make this triangle.

How many pencils do you think you will need to make the next size triangle?

Check your prediction by making the triangle.

How about the next size up?

GO FOR IT!

This square has been made with 4 pencils.

How many pencils will you need to make the next size square?

21

3D Skeleton Shapes

Get Ready

You will need:
- Cocktail sticks
- Modelling clay

Skeleton shapes are not spooky. They are just shapes made from sticks and modelling clay!

Faces

This is a cube. A cube is a solid, or **three-dimensional (3D)**, shape.

The sides of the cube are called **faces**.

This is the skeleton of a cube.

Take some cocktail sticks and modelling clay and make your own skeleton cube.

How many sticks do you need?

How many balls of modelling clay?

Four's Fantastic Facts

The parts of the skeleton created by the sticks are called the **edges** of the shape.

The places where there are balls of modelling clay are the **vertices**.

Can you make skeletons for each of these shapes using cocktail sticks and balls of modelling clay?

Cuboid

Square-based pyramid

Triangular prism

How many edges will your cuboid have?

How many vertices will your square-based pyramid have?

Can you make a skeleton shape with exactly 6 sticks and 4 balls of modelling clay?

Go For It!

Look at these 3D shapes.

Sphere

Cylinder

Can you find objects in your home or classroom that are the same shape as a sphere or a cylinder?

Paper Patterns

Have fun with this activity folding, predicting and cutting.

Get Ready

You will need:
- Lots of squares of paper (you can use scrap paper or paper that's been written on)
- Scissors
- Paper and a pen or pencil

1. Take a square of paper and fold it in half.

2. Next, fold the paper in half again.

3. Now you are going to cut off the corner of the paper like this.

4. Before you make the cut, draw a sketch of the shape you think you are going to make by cutting the paper.

5. Cut off the corner and open up the folds.

Was your sketch correct?

6. Take another square of paper. Make the same two folds as before. Then make a third fold.

What shape do you think will be made when you cut off the point?

Draw a sketch of your prediction. Make the cut and open up the folds.

GO FOR It!

Can you find a way to fold and cut your paper to make a 6-sided shape?

How about an 8-pointed star?

Gnome Homes

Get Ready

You will need:
• Modelling clay

Gnomes live in homes made out of exactly four cubes.

Gnomes build their houses by joining the faces, or sides, of cubes exactly.

This is a gnome home.

This is not.

Gnomes like their houses to be only one storey high. They do not stack cubes on top of each other.

So this is a gnome home.

But this is not.

Try building some gnome homes out of modelling clay.

GO For It!

Try building some bigger gnome homes using five cubes.

Your cubes don't have to be big. About the size of a large dice is perfect.

How many different gnome homes can you make?

Flying Fish

Try making a series of fish shapes that fit together.

Get Ready

You will need:

- A square of cardboard (about 10 cm x 10 cm)
- Scissors
- Sticky tape
- A large sheet of paper
- Coloured pencils or pens

1 Draw a line from one side of the square of cardboard to the opposite side.

Make the line look a little like the head of a fish.

2 Cut along the line to make two pieces.

3 Now swap the positions of the two pieces and join them with sticky tape.

4 Now lay your cardboard fish shape on the large piece of paper. Draw around the shape.

Then move the shape to a new position so it fits exactly with the fish outline you've just drawn.

5 Keep drawing around the cardboard shape to make lots of outlines that all fit together.

Decorate your flying fish!

Four's Fantastic Facts

Shapes that fit together like this are called tessellating shapes. A famous artist called M.C. Escher made lots of pictures like yours.

Can you see the lizards in this tessellation pattern?

Curve Stitching

You will need:
- A sheet of paper
- A ruler
- Coloured pens or pencils

Each line should be 10 cm long.

Mark each centimetre on the two lines and number the marks from 1 to 10.

Draw two lines on your sheet of paper.

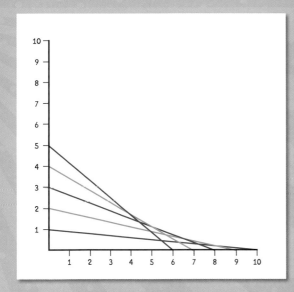

Now begin joining the points on each line that add up to eleven.

Use your ruler and a pen or pencil to join 1 to 10, 2 to 9, 3 to 8 and so on.

What do you notice about the coloured lines?

GO For It!

Now draw a square that's 10 cm x 10 cm. Mark each centimetre on the four sides of the square. Then start joining the pairs of numbers that add up to eleven.

Can you make a curve in every corner of your square?

Let's Play Buried Treasure

Get Ready

You will need:
- Counters or buttons
- A book to stand up as a screen
- Paper and pens or pencils (for recording guesses)
- A friend to play with

Get ready to hunt for buried treasure on a desert island!

(1) Each player chooses to play on one of the boards on page 29.

(2) Stand a book between the two boards, like a screen, so the players can't see their opponent's board.

(3) Each player puts four pieces of treasure (counters) on four different squares on their board.

(4) Now the players must take turns to guess where their opponent's treasure is buried. For example:

Player One: "Is there treasure in square A3?"

If A3 is correct, Player Two says **"Green"** and gives Player One the treasure.

If A3 is one square away from treasure, Player Two says **"Orange"**.

If the guess is any other square, Player Two says **"Red"**.

(5) Now it's Player Two's turn to pick a square, and Player One must say whether it's Green, Orange or Red.

(6) The winner is the first player to collect all their opponent's treasure!

Can you find a way to record your guesses to help you find the treasure?

 You can download the game boards for printing out here: www.rubytuesdaybooks.com/goforit

Tips for Maths Success

Page 4:   Line Designs

This activity will help your child explore the different two-dimensional shapes that can be made from straight lines. Once they have coloured some of the shapes, you can talk about the names that we give shapes.

Page 5:   Shape Hunt

Being able to see shapes within other shapes is a skill that will help your child in lots of future mathematics. There are 17 rectangles to be found (including the big one) and 8 triangles (including the big one).

Page 6:   Take 4 Triangles

The four triangles can be used to make:

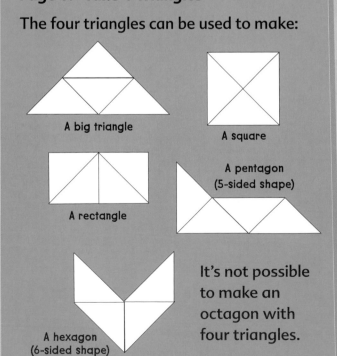

A big triangle

A square

A rectangle

A pentagon (5-sided shape)

A hexagon (6-sided shape)

It's not possible to make an octagon with four triangles.

Page 7:   Two-Piece Tangram

A two-piece tangram can be used to make the following shapes:

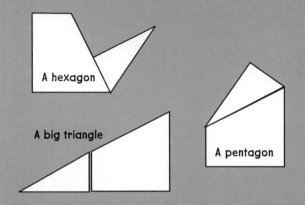

A hexagon

A big triangle

A pentagon

It's not possible to make a rectangle or octagon from the tangram.

Pages 8—9:   Follow My Lead

This activity will help your child refine three key aspects of the language of shape and space: describing shapes *(take the small green square)*, orientation *(turn it so that it looks like a diamond)* and position *(put it to the right-hand side of the circle)*.

Page 10:   Fill the Grid

Coordinating two properties — in this case colour and shape — is another skill that will be helpful and useful to your child. Once they have filled the grid you could play "what's my shape?" Take it in turns to think of one of the nine shapes and the other player has to figure out what it is by asking questions that only have a YES or NO answer.

Page 11: Midpoint Patterns

It's fine to guess the midpoints of the sides of the shapes. But if your child is ready to use a ruler, show them how to use it to measure the sides of the shapes and to halve that length to mark the midpoints accurately.

Pages 12—13: Exploded Square

Some scientists think that we are born with an innate sense of symmetry. This activity and the projects on pages 14 and 15 will help your child refine that sense. Exploded Square is a great introduction to the concept of symmetry. Your child's pattern can be as simple or intricate as they like, but they will soon see that both sides will always be symmetrical.

Pages 14—15: Exploring Symmetry

If you have a colour printer, it's fun to look at the symmetry of your child's face. Take a photo of your child and print it out. Then flip the image and print that version (so you have a mirror image of the original picture).

Cut each picture in half and then make two new faces from the two left sides and the two right sides.

Each new face will be perfectly symmetrical. Which face does your child like best?

Page 16: Birthday Card Jigsaw

If you're playing with your child, it can be helpful to "play dumb". You might know what your child means, but if their instruction is not completely clear, then playfully get it wrong. For example, if they say, "Put that piece by the first piece," put it above the first piece, even though you know they meant for it to be placed at the side. When you get the instruction wrong, they will have to think again about the words they are using and make their instruction clearer.

Page 17: Build a Box

You may need to do a little advance preparation here. Many cereal boxes have two flaps that connect to make the lid. Cut one of these flaps off and tape it to the other so that there are six rectangles when the box is cut apart.

Pages 18—19: What's My Shape?

This fun guessing game requires logic. You might need to help your child appreciate the power of negative answers. For example, there might only

Pages 18—19: continued

be squares and circles left on the board. "Is it a square?" the child asks. You answer "No". Rather than realising that this means it must be a circle, they may think getting the answer wrong is not helpful and go on to ask, "Is it a circle?"

Pages 20—21: Square & Triangle Challenge

You can make 9 squares with 20 pencils. Here are two ways:

Here is the growing triangle and square.

Pages 22—23: 3D Skeleton Shapes

While making the skeleton shapes talk about the number of corners and edges the 3D skeletons have and encourage your child to visualise the sides being filled in to count the number of faces. You can make a tetrahedron with 6 sticks and 4 balls of modelling clay.

Page 24: Paper Patterns

Visualising (picturing shapes in your head) is important when working with shapes and space. This activity will engage your child in visualising. If you do it together, talk about what you think

the shape is going to be and how you are figuring that out before unfolding it. You can also explore how many different ways the cut-out piece can be fitted back into the hole in the square of paper.

Page 25: Gnome Homes

When investigating which gnome home shapes are possible talk about what counts as different. Ask, "Are these two houses the same or different?" There is no correct answer. The important thing is for your child to come up with reasons for why the shapes are different or are not.

Page 26: Flying Fish

Look up the work of M.C. Escher online. Your child may be inspired to make some more detailed tessellations.

Page 27: Curve Stitching

There is something magical about the way a curve emerges out of drawing straight lines. A square with a curve in each corner should look like this.

Pages 28—29: Let's Play Buried Treasure

This game will introduce your child to coordinates. The convention is to go along first and then up, so encourage your child to say B2 rather than 2B.